More Adventures of the
SUPERKIDS

D1529680

STUDENT BOOK UNITS 3–4

Name

THE SUPERKIDS READING PROGRAM

FIRST GRADE

More Adventures of the
SUPERKIDS

BY PLEASANT T. ROWLAND

ILLUSTRATED BY LORETTA LUSTIG, MERYL HENDERSON & DOUG ROY

CONTRIBUTING WRITER: VALERIE TRIPP

DEVELOPED BY ROWLAND READING FOUNDATION

For the convenience of teachers and parents, this book contains abbreviated citations of the Common Core State Standards, noted in pink at the bottom of each page. The complete standards are available online at *superkidsreading.org*.

ISBN: 978-1-61436-226-5   MO36226.0315   2 3 4 5 6 4495 19 18 17 16 15

UNITS   1–2   3–4   5–6   7–8   9–10

Unit 3

1. he is
   he's
   he's

2. she is
   she's
   she's

3. it is
   it's
   it's

4. I am
   I'm
   I'm

5. we are
   we're
   we're

6. you are
   you're
   you're

7.
He is
_____
_____
_____

running fast.

8.
She is
_____
_____
_____

riding a bike.

9.
It is
_____
_____
_____

lunch time.

10.
I am
_____
_____
_____
Cass.

11.

We are
_____
_____
_____
the Superkids!

12.
You are
_____
_____
_____
a super kid too!

1

It is

1. _It's_____ a box of dress-up stuff.

I am

2. _____ a cook.

He is

3. _____ a king.

She is

4. _____ a queen.

We are

5. _____ chickens.

You are

6. _____ a monster.

Structural Analysis, Spelling
RF.1.3, L.1.2e

Parents: Your child traced X's and apostrophes at the top of the page and then completed sentences by writing a contraction for each pair of words shown above the lines.

I will	he will	she will	we will	you will	it will
I̶ ̶w̶i̶l̶l̶	h̶e̶ ̶w̶i̶l̶l̶	s̶h̶e̶ ̶w̶i̶l̶l̶	w̶e̶ ̶w̶i̶l̶l̶	y̶o̶u̶ ̶w̶i̶l̶l̶	i̶t̶ ̶w̶i̶l̶l̶
I'll	he'll	she'll	we'll	you'll	it'll

We want something new to do.

She will

1. Let's ask Gert. *She'll* tell us what we can do.

I will
_____

2. I have a plan. _____ take you on a trip.

you will
_____

3. Where? I bet _____ take us to a fun spot!

We will
_____   **It will**
_____

4. _____ go to Happy Land. _____ be fun!

He will
_____

5. Fantastic! Let's tell Gus. _____ want to come.

Structural Analysis; Grammar, Usage, and Mechanics; Spelling
RF.1.3, L.1.2, L.1.2e

Trickers

lāzy   pony   pāper   mŭsic

The Superkids are going to Happy Land.
What do you think will happen?

rope   open
_____

□ 1. Happy Land will be _____ .

ladder   lazy
_____

□ 2. The Superkids will be too _____ to go on the rides

pony   poke
_____

□ 3. The kids will see a _____ in the Animal Shed.

slipper   super
_____

□ 4. The kids will have a _____ day.

over   shady   tiny   baby

sheep shady

☐ 5. The kids will eat lunch under a _____ tree.

tiny tent

☐ 6. The kids will see a little _____ pig.

baby bumpy

☐ 7. The kids will cry like a _____ in the Monster Tunnel.

off over

☐ 8. The kids will be happy when the day is _____ .

Phonics, Vocabulary, Spelling
RF.1.3, SL.1.4, SL.1.1a, L.1.2e

1. pony   peach   penny

2. sunny   shady   silly

3. bat   bunny   baby

4. tiger   time   tell

5. tricky   tiny   tan

6. lazy   let   late

Parents: On this page and page 7, your child circled the word that describes each picture.

1.

music   messy   muddy

2.

pickle   pilot   pie

3.

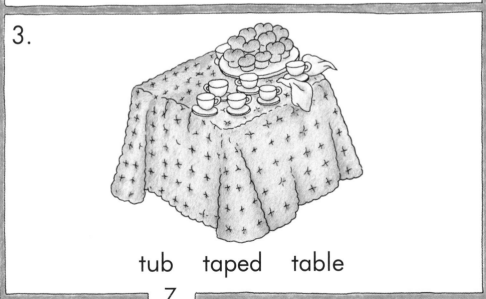

tub   taped   table

7

Long-Vowel Trickers

paper

even

silent

open

music

Parents: Help your child memorize the spelling of these tricky long-vowel words. Each word will be on the Unit 3 spelling test.

Contractions

Put the words together. Drop 1 or 2 letters from the second word. Add an **'**.

's

he is → he's
she is → she's
it is → it's

'm

I am → I'm

're

we are → we're
you are → you're

'll

I will → I'll
he will → he'll
she will → she'll
we will → we'll
you will → you'll
it will → it'll

Parents: Help your child practice spelling the contractions on this list. Five of these contractions will be on the Unit 3 spelling test.

Parents: Your child wrote words from the top of each box to complete phrases describing objects and characters from a story they've read, "A Super Day at Happy Land."

fluffy   junky   tiny

1. a _____ pig

2. a _____ doll

3. a _____ hat

yummy   sleepy   shady

4. a _____ tree

5. a _____ hot dog

6. _____ Superkids

8

Spelling; Grammar, Usage, and Mechanics
L.1.2e, L.1.1f

1.

Frits and Doc got wet on the ride.

Frits and Doc got fish on the ride.

2.

Sal got the best prize because he tipped over the bottles.

Ettabetta got the best prize because she did not tip over the bottles.

3.

There were tigers and acrobats at the Animal Shed.

There was a tiny pig named Taffy at the Animal Shed.

4.

Hot Rod and Ettabetta were afraid at the top of the Ferris wheel.

Hot Rod and Ettabetta liked getting stuck at the top of the Ferris wheel.

5.

The Superkids ate hot dogs under a shady tree.

The Superkids ate hot dogs under a blanket.

Comprehension
RL.1.1

6.

A sleeping trash can ate Alf's trash.

A speaking trash can ate Alf's trash.

7.

Gert and Gus looked silly on the Lucky Ducky.

Gert and Gus looked angry on the Lucky Ducky.

8.

Tac and Oswald got lazy from the Twist-Up.

Tac and Oswald got dizzy from the Twist-Up.

9.

The Streak was a speedy, hilly ride.

The Streak was a chilly, silly ride.

10.

The Superkids were sleepy after a rotten day at Happy Land.

The Superkids were sleepy after a super day at Happy Land.

Parents: Your child completed sentences by writing a contraction for each pair of words shown above the lines and then wrote in the small box next to each picture the number of the sentence that describes the picture.

we are

1. Yippee, _____ at Happy Land!

I will

2. _____ bring my swimsuit next time.

I am

3. _____ crazy about this treat!

He will

4. That's Cubby. _____ eat your trash.

It is

5. _____ The Streak, the fastest ride.

Structural Analysis; Comprehension; Spelling; Grammar, Usage, and Mechanics

1. The Superkids had a terrific time at Happy Land.

   ○ wonderful   ○ rotten

2. Gus and Gert looked silly on the Lucky Ducky.

   ○ funny   ○ angry

3. Sal got a fluffy monster doll.

   ○ lazy   ○ fuzzy

4. The Superkids liked the tiny pig.

   ○ soft   ○ itty-bitty

5. The Streak is a fast ride.

   ○ speedy   ○ past

6. Tac and Oswald kept giggling.

   ○ crying   ○ chuckling

Parents: Your child read each sentence, identified the meaning of the pink word, and filled in the bubble next to the word below that means almost the same thing.

Vocabulary
L15

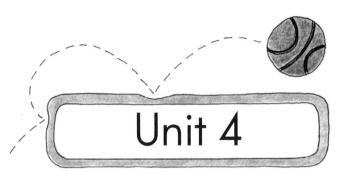

Unit 4

1.

Aw, shucks!

2.

Aw, shucks!

Cass <u>saw</u> a big mess.

3.

Aw, shucks!

Yawn! Sal is still sleepy.

4.

Aw, shucks!

Golly cut his paw.

5.

Aw, shucks!

Her claws are stuck.

Parents: Your child identified the word in each sentence that has the sound heard at the end of the word saw; underlined the letters that stand for that sound, aw; and told why each character said or thought, "Aw, shucks!"

13

Phonemic Awareness, Phonics
RF.1.2c, RF.1.3, RF.1.3b

draw   saw   straw   awful   crawl

1. Doc uses her _____ .

2. Ettabetta likes to _____ .

3. The baby likes to _____ .

4. Tac drinks from a _____ .

5. Lily smells an _____ smell!

Parents: Your child underlined aw in the words at the top of the page and then wrote those words to complete sentences about the pictures.

Phonics, Vocabulary
RF.1.3b, L.1.4a

Pattern Words

all

tall　ball　wall　hall

1.

Don't fall over a

_____

_____

_____ .

2.

Call down the

_____

_____

_____ .

3.

Let's all play

_____

_____

_____ .

4.

Is he small or

_____

_____

_____ ?

Phonemic Awareness, Phonics, Vocabulary, Spelling
RF.1.2c, RF.1.3, RF.1.3b, L.1.4, L.1.2d, L.1.2e

and then wrote those words to complete sentences about the pictures.

all

call
fall
small

aw

law
saw
draw

awn

dawn
lawn
yawn

awl

bawl
crawl
shawl

Parents: Help your child practice spelling words that follow patterns. Five of these words will be on the Unit 4 spelling test.

Memory Words

Parents: Help your child memorize the spelling of these Memory Words. Each word will be on the Unit 4 spelling test.

come

coming

they

our

put

to read and spell the Memory Words at the top of the page.

come   coming   they   our   put

Basketball Fans!

Come! Come! Come!

The Super Hawks are coming!

They are the champs!

They will be at our mall!

Look at them put the ball in the basket!

Play Ball! Play Ball!

16

Parents: Your child completed each sentence by choosing one of two words and writing it on the lines.

claw   wall
_____
_____

1. Doc painted the _____ green.

calls   claws
_____
_____

2. The cat scratches with her _____ .

hall   hawk
_____
_____

3. Hot Rod hung his jacket in the _____ .

small   bawl
_____
_____

4. Tac began to _____ .

crawled   called
_____
_____

5. Tic _____ Alf to come over and play.

17

Phonics, Spelling
RF.1.3, RF.1.3b, L.1.2d, L.1.2e

1. At the mall, the Superkids saw

_____
_____
_____
_____
_____
_____

2. The game stopped when the ball

_____
_____
_____
_____
_____

3. Lily helped the Super Hawks by

_____
_____
_____
_____
_____

4. At the end, the kids and the Super Hawks

_____
_____
_____

Parents: Your child completed sentences to tell what happened in the story "Play Ball!"

Comprehension
RL.1.1, RL.1.3, L.1.1j

Parents: In each row, your child read about two events from the story "Play Ball!" and wrote 1 by the event that happened first and 2 by the event that happened second.

Which was first? ☐1 Which was second? ☐2

☐ The Superkids got a new basketball.

☐ The Superkids went to the mall.

☐ Number 7 tripped and fell. The ball popped from his hands.

☐ The Super Hawks' ball got stuck at the top of the mall.

☐ The Super Hawks and the Superkids played basketball.

☐ Lily handed the Superkids' basketball to Number 7.

Comprehension
RL.1.2, RL.1.7

1. What was the problem with the Superkids' bus?
   - ○ It tipped over in a big wind.
   - ○ It was messy with litter and junk all over.

2. Why did the kids fix up the bus?
   - ○ to win a contest
   - ○ to go on a trip

3. Where had the kids seen Rex King before?
   - ○ playing ball at the mall
   - ○ on his TV show

4. What did Rex King look like?
   - ○ He was a little man with freckles.
   - ○ He was a tall man with a big smile.

5. When did Golly jump up on Rex King?
   - ○ when Rex was crawling
   - ○ when Rex said, "My golly!"

6. Why did the Superkids get to be on TV?
   - ○ They played in a basketball game.
   - ○ They won the Grand Land Contest.

Parents: Your child answered questions about the story "Play Ball!" by filling in the bubble next to the correct answer for each question.

Comprehension
RL.1.1

Parents: Your child read Memory Words at the top of the page and used them to complete sentences about the story "Rex King's Visit." The sentences include rebuses, which are pictures that stand for words.

come	coming	They	our	put

1.  and his helpers are _____ .

2. _____ are looking for land that looks grand.

3. We will fix up _____  .

4. We will _____ an 🎪 and a 🌸 on it.

5. Then we will be set for  to _____ .

Vocabulary, Comprehension, Spelling
RF.1.3g, RL.1.7, RL.1.1, RL.1.10, L.1.2d

1.

○ The Superkids like a big mess.

○ The Superkids do not like litter.

2.

○ Ettabetta thinks plants look rotten.

○ Ettabetta thinks plants look good.

3.

○ All the Superkids want to help when there is work to do.

○ Frits and Alf never want to help when there is work to do.

4.

○ Golly thinks Rex King is mean.

○ Golly thinks Rex King is his pal.

5.

○ The Superkids were glad to be on TV.

○ The Superkids were sad to be on TV.

Parents: In each row, your child filled in the bubble next to the sentence that tells about the picture and the story "Rex King's Visit."

Parents: Your child cut out words and glued or taped them over words that have opposite meanings to make the sentences tell what happened in the story "Rex King's Visit."

1. Rex King is ⬛ leaving ⬛ .

2. The Superkids ⬛ mess up ⬛ the bus.

3. Sal ⬛ takes down ⬛ the awning.

4. Cass puts a bench ⬛ over ⬛ the awning.

5. The Superkids' bus looks ⬛ awful ⬛ .

Vocabulary
L.1.5

under	puts up	fix up
grand	coming	

Draw it!

1.

Draw a line over the taller Super Hawk.

2.

Put an X on the Superkid cutting the lawn.

3.

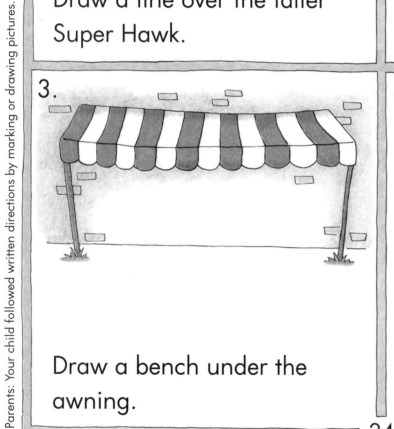

Draw a bench under the awning.

4.

Go team!

Draw a fan calling "Go team!"

24

Phonics
RF.1.3b

Parents: Your child wrote sentences about a favorite TV show.

1. The best TV show I ever saw was

2. I liked it when

Writing; Grammar, Usage, and Mechanics
W.1.1, L.1.1j, L.1.2

Parents: Your child found, traced, and circled spelling words from Units 3–4 to complete the puzzle.

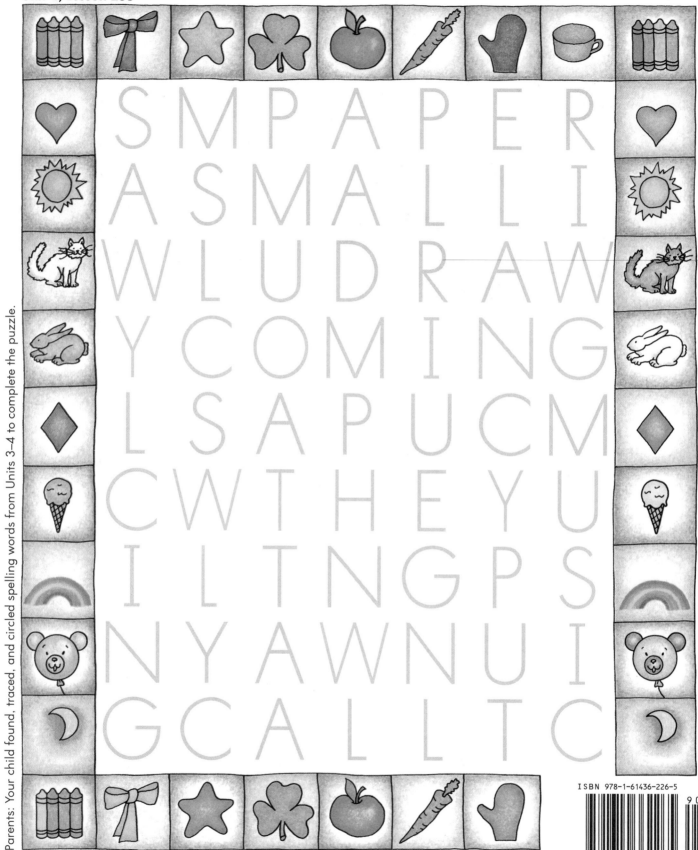

ISBN 978-1-61436-226-5

ZB Zaner-Bloser

1-800-421-3018

www.zaner-bloser.com

MO36226